So What's Wrong With a Big Nose?

Building Self-Esteem

Fran & Jill Sciacca

ZondervanPublishingHouse
Grand Rapids, Michigan

A Division of HarperCollinsPublishers

Requests for information should be addressed to:
Zondervab Publishing House
Grand Rapids, Michigan 49530

ISBN: 0-310-48051-5

Printed in the United States of America

92 93 94 95 96 / DP / 5 4 3 2 1

Why "Lifelines"?

Who in the world are Fran and Jill ... is it Sky-ocka??

The name "Sciacca" (actually pronounced "Shock-a") is probably not a familiar name to you. Let me take you on a quick trek through our lives so you will know who we are and why we care so much about you.

Fran grew up in the shadow of older identical twin brothers who were football stars. While their photos and accomplishments appeared regularly in newspapers and magazines, Fran found himself wondering who he was besides "the twins' little brother." In high school, he decided to take his talents "elsewhere," completely out of the arena of athletics; he set out to become the best bass guitarist he could be. His rock band was a success, and soon Fran also made it to the pages of the newspaper. On one occasion he played in front of 5,000 people at a "battle of the bands" in Milwaukee, Wisconsin. Fame became Fran's total focus in his search for "self." He was popular at school and was elected class president for three years.

In college, Fran quickly blazed his way to the top of his fraternity. The professional status of his new rock group also gave him personal pride. The band's popularity soared beyond the college campus, and Fran began doing "warm-up" for nationally known entertainers such as Chase and B. J. Thomas. He had finally "arrived" —or so he thought. But why, he wondered, was the feeling of emptiness still lodged so deep in his soul?

Then in one year's time the band began to break up, his girlfriend dumped him, and he received the devastating news that one of his brothers had been seriously wounded in the Vietnam War. It was as if someone had let the air out of his world. He felt alone in the universe. Even his 12 years of religious education in a private school didn't help him.

About this time, God brought a friend into Fran's life who had just committed his own life to Jesus Christ. Late one night in a quiet dorm room, Fran heard from him about the depth of God's love. For the first time, Fran had reason to believe that he was a valuable person, not because he was "cool," or a popular bass guitarist, but because the God of the universe loved him and had paid the penalty for his sin. Fran found the identity he had always longed for in the person of Jesus Christ.

Jill's Journey

I grew up in the "suburbs," graduating with a class of more than 700 students. My years in high school could best be characterized by my quest to know, "Where's the party?" But when I was alone, I often thought about life and death—even suicide. I wrote poems that exposed my inner fears but felt they were "safe" as simple assignments for English class. As best I could, I squelched my spiritual emptiness by dancing, partying, working a little, and playing a lot.

My folly and flippant approach to study in high school forced me to be on probation for the first quarter of college. I buckled down to get good grades but somehow managed to maintain my carefree lifestyle "to the max." I was dating a gifted art student, and together with other friends we embraced the sixties' counterculture. Our philosophy boasted that peace was possible; we could affect society and bring about lasting change. "We" were the answer to all of America's problems.

Yet in two years' time I witnessed the tragic folly of the sixties' philosophy in vivid detail: A best friend from high school had burned out on drugs. Another had died while on drugs. I had seen that our protests against the Vietnam War were leading to prison sentences. People were losing heart. Dropping out. My boyfriend had been committed to a psychiatric ward in a hospital. My best girlfriend, who had entered college on a scholarship, had quit, disillusioned with life. My rock star heroes had fallen from the thrones I'd placed them on. Jimi Hendrix had died. (I had been in the front rows at one of his concerts.) Jim Morrison was gone. Drugs and death seemed to go together. We were not the answer to America's woes—we were part of the problem!

So I fled from the fast lane and started studying philosophy, searching for answers but finding none. Finally, I desperately cried out to the God I had learned about in Sunday school as a child. I had always believed in him but never realized that I could know him personally. Committing my life to him, I made him my Lord and found the peace I hadn't found in all my searching. I joined the ranks of the revival on our college campus, the one that had also swept Fran into the faith. We were radical, but now we had an anchor and a purpose that was really destined to succeed.

And Then, Fran & Jill

We were married after graduation from college. Our first home was in Wisconsin, out in the country, where we attended a small church. There we immediately gravitated to the youth. Three years and one son later, the Lord led us to Denver, Colorado, where Fran went to seminary. While in Denver, we were again drawn to teens as Fran did field work at a local church. Two years and another son later, the Lord led us to Colorado Springs Christian School, where Fran has been teaching Bible in high school ever since! Now we also have the blessed bonus of twin daughters.

We need to tell you all of this for two reasons: First, everything that these studies deal with comes out of our own experience. Second, in many of the things that you're going to look at in *Lifelines: Bible Studies for Students*, we totally "blew it." So not only do we understand the issues at hand, we also know the pain and temptation that go with the territory.

We believe that a genuine relationship with Jesus Christ and with those who are committed to him is the most fulfilling and exciting thing on this sometimes perplexing planet! We're not talking about people who "play church." We're talking about those who are really serious about falling in love with and following the One who died for us.

So be assured that your struggles are familiar to us. They are foes that we have fought too. They are battles that we often lost. But we know there is a way of victory, and we want to help you discover that door of hope.

We pray that, through a personal study of God's Word, you will gain a new vision for a meaningful life, walking with the Lord and living in victory.

Fran and I are a "fun" team. He is the "architect"; I am the "builder." You will find the Bible study section of each chapter designed by Fran. I have helped Fran put a "personal touch" to the studies by telling a story you can relate to, about someone who has been a part of our lives. (Names, gender, and nonessential details have been altered to protect the privacy of those involved.)

There is one more thing we want you to know as you begin this Bible study—we really care about you!

What Is "Lifelines"?

Life is tough! Being a teenager is even tougher. You bounce somewhere between adulthood and childhood, ping-ponging back and forth, not really landing on either side, never really knowing which side you're supposed to be on at any given moment. The temptation to give in or give up may seem greater than you can bear. You probably feel as if you're sinking in a sea of pressures and problems too deep and wide to navigate. Let's face it, life's a battle. But ... on the other hand, is that so unusual?

What does it take to make the first-string soccer team? What's the cost of working your way to first-chair trumpet in the school band? How long did you have to practice to become the best guitarist at school? Remember those early-morning practices for the spring play? It seems as if everything significant has a price tag. Maybe that's the way it's supposed to be; maybe that's the way God planned it. But he also provides the help we need along the way. *Lifelines: Bible Studies for Students* is one of those helpers.

"Lifelines" Is Different

Lifelines: Bible Studies for Students is different. It won't help you "sail" through life, because nobody sails through life. But *Lifelines* will be honest with you about life, about God, about yourself, about your choices and your dreams. *Lifelines* promises "to put the cookies on the bottom shelf," to meet you right where you are and deal with the things that you have to deal with each day. It promises to provide answers where there are answers and to ask questions where they need to be asked.

But, just as in the rest of life, there are some costs that go with these Bible studies. What are they? Simply this: *Lifelines: Bible Studies for Students* promises to be honest with you, but you've got to be honest with yourself. And even more important—you've got to be honest with God. These studies are built on the presupposition that the Bible is God's Word. That means that your opinions and feelings have a genuine place in your life, but the final place is reserved for God's Word.

This Bible study cannot change your life; only God can do that. But, God can't guide a parked car. You're the one who's got to cooperate with God as you carefully work through this study.

You've got to be willing to let the Lord into your life, into your problems and pressures, into your battle. He wants to be beside you whether you are defeated or determined. If you are willing to pay this price, *Lifelines: Bible Studies for Students* could very well be one of the most exciting things that happens to you this year!

Things to Keep in Mind:

Here are some important thoughts to keep in mind as you begin:

#1 God is not a coach. He doesn't have a checklist for your performance. He loves you. In fact, he loves you just as you are as you begin this study.

#2 Apply what you learn to yourself. Resist the urge to think of others who "really need to hear" what you are learning.

#3 Be faithful. Whatever your commitment is, whether to a group or simply to yourself, keep it. Make it your goal to finish the study.

#4 Be realistic. Weeds grow quickly, but an oak tree takes time. Look for small ways to grow. If you set goals that are too tough, you'll become discouraged. Small victories will encourage you to keep going.

Lifelines: Bible Studies for Students accepts the fact that much of life is a battle for you. But, you can win.

> You've got to know there's a bigger plan.
> Room to fall, room to stand.
> Pray for the plan to begin in you.
> Keep your heart true!*
>   [sung by Amy Grant]

God wants you to win the battle, but remember: You can't have a victory where there's been no fight. You may fall—we all do—but learn to stand!

*"Who to Listen To" by Gary Chapman, Tim Marsh, and Mark Wright.
© 1985 Blackwood Music, Inc./Land of Music/Riverstone Music, Inc.

How to Use This Bible Study

This Bible study is part of a series entitled *Lifelines: Bible Studies for Students.* Each study in the series centers around a single issue that you, as a teenager, face in the twentieth century. This study, *So What's Wrong with a Big Nose?*, deals with the subject of self-esteem—how you view yourself.

We really wish we could promise that this study will answer all the questions and heal all the hurts you have in the area of how you view yourself. But we can't. In fact, we both still struggle with accepting ourselves the way God made us, and we're in our late thirties!

So why do a Bible study on self-esteem? Well, for one thing, we think you'll find in these pages some vital (and possibly radical!) ideas as you struggle with this issue. If you take these ideas seriously and the suggestions for action that go with them, then you'll be light-years ahead of *us* in your search for self-worth.

Each chapter of *So What's Wrong with a Big Nose?* includes a real-life story, some personal study questions, and a summary discussion. Look for one major truth, a "Lifeline," as you go through each chapter. If there are specific things the study asks you to do, be sure to do them. The personal insights you pull out of these pages won't help you until you begin to put them into practice.

The only things you will need to complete this study are a Bible, a pen, and an open heart. We suggest that you use the *New International Version* or *The Living Bible.* Make sure that your Bible has both the Old and the New Testaments. We suggest you also have a spiral notebook to record thoughts and ideas that come to you while you study.

If you study *So What's Wrong with a Big Nose?* in a group, you'll find the optional group discussion questions in each chapter's "Bottom Line" section enlightening and helpful.

There is another optional section near the end of each chapter, entitled "His Lines." These are two passages from the Bible that might be helpful as you seek to make the "Lifeline" from that chapter a reality in your own life. You can memorize these verses, put them on your mirror, in your locker, or on the dashboard of your car. Plant them anyplace where they can prompt you to remember the truth when you need it the most.

Other Lifelines

If you enjoy *So What's Wrong with a Big Nose?*, you may want to try these other *Lifelines* studies:

Are Families Forever?
Strengthening Family Ties

Burgers, Fries & a Friend to Go
Making Friends

Cliques & Clones
Facing Peer Pressure

Does Anyone Else Feel This Way?
Conquering Loneliness and Depression

Good News for a Bad News World
Understanding the Gospel

Is This the Real Thing?
What Love Is and Isn't

What Really Matters?
Setting Priorities

1

The Hurt No One Talks About

Opening Lines

If I had been asked after my first semester to evaluate the career of teaching high school students, I would have compared it to the suffering of Job. Man, was it tough! Trying to get to know my new flock of kids, I joined the lunchtime activity of shooting baskets in the gym. This was during the second month of school. A hard fall and a flushed face followed one play of mine. Then later came the declaration from the doctor that I had torn my Achilles' tendon. For the next three months I taught from a wheelchair or on crutches. I fell down stairs on occasion, my crutches were stolen by creative students, and I wore a very heavy cast that kept me from doing anything fun. Finally the cast came off, but for three more months I couldn't run. My right calf muscle looked like a wobbly, canned string bean! I was banished to the bleachers for the rest of the year.

I couldn't play with the students anymore, but I still wanted to get to know them. I wanted to convince them that I could be trusted, that I was teaching them because I cared about them. I knew both the highs and the hazards of being a high school student. They could talk to me. I would listen and try to understand. What I didn't know was that it would take most of the year for them to be convinced that I cared. It did happen, however, and by year's end I felt certain that I'd made some lifelong friends. They believed in me—and I believed in them.

But one thing that happened that year showed me how little I really knew these kids. You would have had to see this class to appreciate what I'm about to tell you. This was one of the most talented, good-looking, fun-loving classes I have ever had. They came from poor families, rich families, large families, small families, Christian and non-Christian families. They were not your classic "clone cluster," by any means! One of the girls was an outstanding athlete, averaging about twenty-two points per game in basketball. Another student was a fine pianist, writing his own scores and able to play everything from Beethoven to Billy Joel. There was even one girl who happened to "have it all"—lovely looks, good grades, starting position in three varsity sports and a state championship in piano!

Have you got the picture? They were a "beautiful" bunch. If you had a view of yourself that wasn't too high, these were the people you wanted to be like.

In Bible class one day, we were talking about temptation and sin, and I decided to show them that everybody struggles with certain sins. No one is perfect, even if we can't identify with another's particular problem areas. So I asked them to write secretly on a piece of paper the one thing they struggled with that they thought no one else would know about. They were to pinpoint the area of sin or weakness in their own life that they were convinced they were alone in.

A few people said they couldn't resist cussing, smoking, lust, even stealing. But to my absolute amazement, more than half of the 75 students in my three classes noted dissatisfaction with themselves as their area of greatest struggle! One out of two of these "beautiful" people were living daily with discouragement as they battled low self-esteem!

I was stunned. How could these students, who had everything that the rest of the high school wished for, be unhappy with who they were or how they looked, or both? What in the world could prompt this particular group to view themselves this way? Awards, fantastic grades, and a constant flow of compliments didn't seem to convince these kids of anything. Perhaps you too struggle with the way you see yourself? Why? What causes this problem that seems to cripple so many of us?

On the Lines

This next section may be a little heavy in regard to some of the concepts we want you to grapple with. It's vital that you take your time thinking through the questions personally and seriously. Each chapter of this study is built upon the ones before it, so make sure that you understand the reasons behind the "Lifeline" for each chapter.

One of the first key steps in understanding the problem of an improper view of ourselves (or "low self-worth," as it is often labeled), is to come to grips with just who we are as human beings. Read the Bible verses below and answer the questions based on what you see in the verses.

1. (Genesis 1:24,25,27) What does man have in common with all living things?

_____

2. Which word do you think best describes all living things, in light of the above verses?

☐ animal   ☐ creature   ☐ life form

3. All creatures, both man and animal, have "creature needs." What are the most basic creature needs?

_____

4. What happens to creatures if their creature needs are not met?

_____

5. Look up Isaiah 41:10. Which word do you think best fits God's description of himself?

☐ impersonal   ☐ personal

6. Look up Genesis 1:27, 5:1 and James 3:9. How is man *different* from the rest of creation?

_____

7. If God is *personal,* and you and I are made in his image, what word *best* describes us?

   ☐ creatures   ☐ persons   ☐ human beings

8. We said above that one result of being a creature is that people have *creature* needs. What kind of needs result from our being *persons?*

_____

9. If a creature's creature needs are not met, it will die as a creature. If that is true, what do you think will happen to you and me if our "person needs" are not met?

_____

10. Christian counselor Larry Crabb says that every human being has two essential person needs. First of all, we all have a need to be loved with no strings attached. Secondly, we all need to believe that we are important or valuable. He calls these two needs *security* and *significance.* Based on all that you've discovered so far in this chapter, would you say that your own person needs are the result of selfishness, or simply part of what it means to be a human being? Explain your answer.

_____

_____

_____

Between the Lines

1. List the names of three people who you used to think didn't struggle with low self-worth:

_____

_____

_____

2. Now, write out why you know they must have the same struggle you have:

_____

_____

3. Perhaps you have realized through this chapter that your need for self-worth is not the result of some selfish preoccupation—it is the result of how God made you. Stop right now and thank God for creating you as a person, in his own, personal image. Tell him you accept your need for self-worth and no longer want to feel guilty about it. Ask him to make the remainder of this study a life-changing beginning—a time to become whatever it is he has made you to become. Put today's date in the margin next to this section.

Closing Lines

The survey in my class that day was definitely an enlightening exercise! I was totally taken off guard by the results. And you should have seen the looks of surprise on everyone's faces when I reported the results the next day! But there was another reaction that I thought was even more interesting. I saw a sense of relief on many faces too. It was as if a wounded, lone soldier had just stumbled through the woods and found the rest of his company. To learn that they were not alone in their battle for self-worth was a liberating discovery for my students.

It can be a source of strength and not sadness when you realize that your battle for self-worth is universal. Your hurt is everyone's hurt, even if no one talks about it. But even more, the need to believe you are somebody—and the need to be unconditionally loved—was put there by a personal God. The needs are real. They are the result of being made in God's image, not of being self-centered.

Lifeline:

My need for self-worth is God-given. It's part of how he made me.

His Lines

Genesis 1:27

Acts 17:28

The Bottom Line (For Group Discussion)

1. Have everyone in the group who has one take out his or her driver's license, and pass them around. Discuss why everyone is unhappy with the picture on theirs.

2. What does it mean to be made in God's image or likeness? Does it have to do with physical features or non-material aspects or both?

3. If everyone has a need for a sense of self-worth, why does it seem to be more of a problem in America than in Third World countries?

4. Why don't people discuss these feelings more often with each other?

5. How do you think people try to mask these feelings? What are some of the things they do?

6. How can we help people open up about their true feelings about themselves? What do we do that causes people to retreat further in their fear of sharing who they really are?

7. What are some "laws" that your group can make, and perhaps even write out and sign together, that will help insure that your group is a safe place to be? These could be certain things you will do or not do, say or not say, whenever you are together.

2

The Revolving Door Syndrome

Opening Lines

I had a great deal going for me in high school—at least that's what you would have thought if you had known me. I was elected class president for three consecutive years, I was a member of the National Honor Society and a bass player for one of the best rock bands in our city. When I was only 15, I competed in a state-wide "battle of the bands" held in Milwaukee, Wisconsin. Most of the money I made on our weekend gigs with the band was spent on clothes. Needless to say, my wardrobe was one of my greatest assets. So my high school "scorecard" showed a person who was popular, well dressed, intelligent and destined for a successful life. Certainly I was happy with myself, wasn't I?

Well, if you could have heard the secret thoughts that I said to no one, you would have discovered that this well-dressed, destined-for-success person was an emotional mess on the inside. I was plagued with feelings of inferiority and frustration. The Fran Sciacca that everyone saw was not the real me! The outer man had charisma; the inner man was crying. I had tried everything I could to make myself happy. And I was a high achiever when it came to popularity, the honor roll, the class presidency, the music, the '66 Mustang, the motorcycle—the list could grind on and on. But I felt as if I was trapped forever in a revolving door. Why weren't these things making me happy? Why did I still hate myself? In spite of all the awards and applause, I was trying to accept myself, or at least to become someone I could admire and accept. Why wasn't it working? My efforts were so fervent. Why were they so futile? What about you? Are you stuck in a revolving door too?

On the Lines

In the last chapter we established that we all have a need for self-worth; we have "person" needs—the need to be loved and to feel important. Let's examine how we normally seek to meet these two needs.

1. Look up the three sets of verses below and write out what you think they show to be the three main sources we use to try to meet our needs for security and self-worth:

SCRIPTURES   SOURCE

A. Luke 18:9-11   _____

B. Revelation 3:17a   _____

C. John 12:42,43;
   Galatians 1:10   _____

2. Now see what each of the following verses says about whether or not the three sources above actually do meet our person needs.

Possible Source A. (see Proverbs 28:26, Romans 7:15,18)
☐ Meets my person needs   ☐ Does not meet my person
                                                  needs

Why/why not? _____

_____

Possible Source B. (see Luke 12:15)
☐ Meets my person needs   ☐ Does not meet my person
                                                  needs

Why/why not? _____

_____

Possible Source C. (see Jeremiah 17:5, Mark 14:50)
☐ Meets my person needs   ☐ Does not meet my person needs

Why/why not? _____

_____

3. Check the phrase or phrases you feel best describe why the three possible sources for meeting your person needs don't work:

    ☐ They are temporary.

    ☐ They have the same problem I have.

    ☐ I never know when I have done enough.

    ☐ They are not measurable.

    ☐ They are too small.

    ☐ They could not provide my real needs even if they wanted to.

4. Looking at your answers to questions 2 and 3 above, what do you think would be the result of trying to have your person needs of security and significance met through any of these three ways? Explain:

_____

_____

_____

Between the Lines

1. Perhaps you have been trying to have your person needs—your need to be loved and to be important—met through things, self, or others. If so, which one is it?

☐ things   ☐ myself   ☐ others

2. How successful have you been? According to your own study, these three sources cannot provide the sense of self-worth that you desire because they are temporary or have the same needs you have or are too small—or perhaps all three. Take some time right now and tell the Lord that you realize you have been trying to provide your own sense of self-worth; and you now know it just isn't possible. Ask him to forgive you, and give you the courage to take the right steps to change.

3. Is there anyone in your life who is looking to you to meet their own needs for security and significance? Perhaps a boyfriend or girlfriend, maybe even a divorced parent. This is one of the quickest ways to destroy a relationship. It places a burden that God never gave a person the strength to handle. If the struggle to provide youself with a sense of self-worth is almost killing you, imagine what it must be like trying to do this for two people! Maybe it's time to let this person know that you care and want to continue your relationship, but that you are feeling a tremendous pressure, beyond your capabilities, to support them emotionally. Find a way, as you brainstorm together, to make the friendship or relationship more healthy and balanced.

Closing Lines

Well, I took my relentless, "revolving door" search for self-worth with me to college. The scene was different, but the act was the same. Again I tried to achieve everything I could. But as before, it all bombed. I was inwardly as hassled as I had been in high school. Maybe even more so, as I didn't have the familiar faces around to cheer me.

I was gradually coming to grips with the fact that I could not provide a sense of self-worth for myself—because I was the problem! That would be like a doctor telling a terminally ill cancer patient to heal herself. Possessions and personal status could not supply a lasting sense of purpose either. They can give only temporary fulfillment; I never really felt I had achieved or accumulated enough. It was an endless cycle. My friends couldn't provide me with a sense of self-worth either, for they were temporary too. Some moved away, one died, others found new friends. And since they had the same problem, how could they help? No, it was quite clear to me that if my sense of self-worth was ever going to be adequate, it would have to come from someone or something outside this world. That doesn't leave a lot of options, does it!

Lifeline:

Neither I nor my surroundings can provide me with a sense of self-worth.

His Lines

Luke 12:15

Proverbs 26:12

The Bottom Line (For Group Discussion)

1. Someone has said, "Persons with a poor sense of self-worth are slaves to the opinions of others." Do you agree or disagree with this statement? Why?

2. How much money do you spend each month trying to get a favorable answer to the question, "How do I look?"

3. Sometimes we let our desire for approval from those "significant others" in our lives cause us to change our behavior or our standards. How do you see this principle operating in the area of sex?

4. Why are girls with poor self-worth often trapped into lowering their moral standards?

5. What does our clothing reveal about our sense of self-worth?

6. What are some of the ways we seek to win the approval of others?

3

"The Love You Can't Lose"

Opening Lines

I had never seen such beauty in all my life—or at least that's what my freshman mind decided. A friend and I were at a big dance in a neighboring town. My object of admiration was smoothly dancing with someone else, but kept looking in my direction. At first I thought I was just dreaming, but it soon became quite evident that she was looking directly at me! I became noticeably nervous. But of course if you're going to convince others that you're cool, you can't let them know your emotions are unraveling like a spool of thread thrown down a staircase! So I stopped trying to capture her attention and casually roamed around the room, sparing her an occasional smile. When you're trying to impress a girl, you've got to make her think you're in control. So I dared not smile too much, or do anything else that would let her know I was churning inside like a locomotive revving up on the tracks—or that my stomach felt as if it had dropped into a food processor and my heart was hammering out a thousand beats per minute.

During one of the band's breaks, her girlfriend and the friend I was with had a brief conversation. When the music resumed, he leaned over to me and said, "She likes you, Sciacca. Go ask her to dance." After about ten minutes of the typical arguments that arise over situations like this, such as, "How do you know for sure?" or, "Yeah, but what if she's just dogging me?" I slid over to her side, and said, "Hi."

That was the beginning of my relationship with Jackie. We dated for almost two years. She was an incredibly popular girl. Her attractiveness, I found, was more the result of her personality than her looks. She had a great sense of humor and the ability to make everyone enjoy being around her. Every year her mother bought yards of material to have Jackie's wardrobe custom tailored. She had been voted best dressed the previous year, in a high school of almost 2,000! Needless to say, I was honored that a girl of her caliber would take an interest in me.

But our relationship began with an enormous amount of uncertainty, because of my own insecurity. I constantly asked myself, "Why would a girl like her be interested in a guy like me?" It never occurred to me that there might be something about me that she found attractive.

I called Jackie every night, sometimes two or three times. Because we went to different schools, I had to make an extra effort to see her both before and after school. We went out every weekend. I didn't like the idea of her having other male friends. I had a terrible time whenever one of them would come up and talk to her when we were out on a date. My jealousy developed into detective work. If I called Jackie and her line was busy, I would look up the phone numbers of guys I knew were interested in her and call their number to see if perhaps she was talking to them. Mistrust developed, causing increasing difficulty and conflict in our relationship. Soon we were fighting all the time, and it was almost always the direct result of my own insecurity.

Jackie and I finally broke up. It was a painful, bitter parting. Why couldn't I trust her? Why did I doubt her devotion to me? Why couldn't I simply accept the fact that she did care enough for me not to be interested in other guys? What was the root of my insecurity? Why do many of us "walk on eggshells" in our relationships, constantly wondering *if* and *why* the other person really cares?

On the Lines

1. Write out what it is about you that you think should make others love you:

_____

_____

2. Write out what it is about you that you think would cause other *not* to love you:

_____

_____

3. Let's examine how God feels about you. Read the following Scripture passage, then rewrite the verses, inserting your name wherever it speaks of someone. (Isaiah 43:1-4)

_____

_____

_____

_____

_____

_____

4. Let's examine exactly what God sees in you, to love you the way he does. Look up Romans 5:6-8. First of all, from these verses how do you know for sure that God loves you? How did he prove his love for you?

_____

Pick the phrase below that best describes what your attitude toward God was at the time he demonstrated his love for you:

☐ I was at my best.   ☐ I was not interested in Him.

☐ I was worth dying for.   ☐ I was at my worst.

5. Pick one of the statements below that you believe best represents what you have discovered from your study so far; defend your answer in the spaces provided:

STATEMENT #1: "I am valuable because God loves me and died for me."

STATEMENT #2: "God loves me and died for me because I am valuable."

MY DEFENSE

_____

_____

_____

_____

_____

6. Let's examine what it would take to lose this love that you did not earn. Read Romans 8:38-40 aloud twice. Below, list all the things that cannot separate you from God's love:

1. _____   2. _____

3. _____   4. _____

5. _____   6. _____

7. _____   8. _____

9. _____   10. _____

7. We said earlier that man's two *person needs* are to be loved (security) and to be somebody (significance). Carefully look back over questions 3—6 and explain in your own words how God himself has already met both of these needs. You may want to review the first chapter of this book before you answer.

_____

_____

_____

_____

_____

8. Look back over Romans 8:38-40 again. Paul describes exactly where this unshakable love is. Where is it?

_____

Can a non-Christian have his person needs met, based on your answer above? Explain.

_____

_____

Between the Lines

1. Realizing that there's nothing you can do to lose God's love for you can become one of the most liberating discoveries of your life. To remind yourself of this truth, write out the following message on a 3x5 card and put it in your locker or on your mirror: *There's nothing I can do to make God stop loving me.*

2. How would you feel if your dad was the president of the Ferrari Corporation or the chairman of the board of the leading clothing manufacturer in the world? What if your dad was a leading political figure attempting to accomplish world peace or raise the standard of living in a Third World country? Listen to this:

> See how very much our heavenly Father loves us, for he allows us to be called his children—think of it—and we really are!...Yes, dear friends, we are already God's children, right now, and we can't even imagine what it is going to be like later on (1 John 3:1,2, TLB).

That's who your "father" is! God! If you are a Christian, the infinite God of the universe is your father! He loves you. He wants to know you inside and out. He is preparing a place for you in heaven right now! God isn't some abstract concept for theologians, he's a personal being who wants you for his child.

Why not take some time right now and kneel down beside your bed or desk. Talk to God as your father. Tell him that you are honestly grateful to be his child. Tell him you realize that being his child makes you of infinite value. Thank him for how valuable you are to him and, because of that, how valuable you are to yourself. Maybe you need a reminder for this idea. Write out the phrase *"Guess who my father is?"* and pin it some place where it will remind you of your value to God whenever your own resources are really low.

Closing Lines

What do you think caused my love for Jackie to shrink, then sour? What had she done to cause me to react that way? The truth of the matter is, she hadn't done a thing. I've looked back on that relationship a lot since then, and have even talked to my wife, Jill, about it. What happened, we've concluded, is a classic illustration of this chapter's lesson. The reason I became resentful and just about crazy during the whole ordeal is that I was never fully convinced that Jackie cared for me. Why? She had never done anything to provoke that conclusion. On the contrary, she had shown lots of signs that she did love me. Our dates were fun and frequent; our phone conversations were constant and characterized by real, deep communication. I was the problem; I was obsessed with finding some value in myself that would merit Jackie's love. But I never could. Our relationship was ripped apart, piece by piece, by my own insecurity and preoccupation with poor self-worth.

For some of you this story is pretty strange, but I also know that there are more than a few of you who have done the same thing. The good news is that you and I are loved and valuable in spite of who we are! The God of all creation loved you when you were at your worst. He went a step further and proved that love by dying for you. If we have truly grasped God's love for us, we should possess a sense of security that enhances all our relationships. If we don't feel secure in the Lord, we will look to other relationships to provide us with the perfect love that only God can give. We will be motivated by fear, and our friendships will most assuredly fail.

But you, my friend, are loved and you are important. The even better news is that there is nothing you can ever do to lose that love. It's yours for keeps if you're really a Christian in right standing with the Lord. Are you?

Lifeline:

God loves me with a love I did not earn and cannot lose.

His Lines

Romans 5:8

1 John 3:1a

The Bottom Line (For Group Discussion)

1. Ask the group to list the people they think are the worst specimens of humanity. They can be living or deceased (i.e., Adolph Hitler). Have them explain why they feel that way. Then have the group react to this statement: "God loves [insert that person's name] as much as he loves you."

2. In what ways do we all seek to earn God's love?

3. Listen to the song, "Clean Before My Lord," by Petra on their *Beat the System* album. How does it relate to the theme of this chapter?

4. How do the truths of this chapter eliminate the idea of someone being proud because of who or what they are? Do you think Christians live and act as though this is true? Explain.

5. An excellent book on this topic is, *His Image—My Image,* by Josh McDowell, published by Here's Life Publishers. Have someone read a chapter of the book each week and report to the group what they feel was the most significant idea in the chapter, and why.

4

Manufacturer's Defects?

Opening Lines

It amazes me how children are able to isolate someone's most distinguishing feature and make it a nickname. It would be bad enough if we endured this type of emotional assault only during grade school; but alas, junior and senior high school students are also reminded of their imperfections, the one or two things about themselves that render them less than equal to Barbie and Ken.

For me, it was my hair. I've got hair that is something of an Afro-American-Italian hybrid. My black friends in college envied me because my hair wasn't as "tight" as theirs, but I could still create an awesome afro (which I did). My white college friends also coveted my mane, because curls like mine cost them $50 every three months at the hair stylist's. But during high school, curly hair for a guy just wasn't in, and my friends made it their sacred duty to remind me of it constantly. I was known, in those days, as "rug head" or "Brillo," just to mention a few flatteries!

Jill had her own struggle in the jungle of name calling. Her nickname was "Nose." I probably don't need to elaborate on the origins of that one! My wife has beautiful eyes. And they were beautiful then. But in high school it's too often your bad points, not your good points, that become the focus for your friends. Jill's other greatest strength was her sensitivity. But her friends often scolded her with statements like, "Oh Jill, you're just too sensitive!"

The result was that Jill grew up believing that she really was too sensitive and that her nose was so long she'd never be noticed beyond its shadow. She began to ask herself questions like, "Why do I have to have such a big nose?" and, "Why can't I be less sensitive, like my friends?" Jill began to question her "design."

And it's a very short distance from questioning your design to questioning the Designer. Why does God make some people the way he does? I mean, why did Jill have to have a larger nose and a greater sensitivity than her friends? Her sensitivity was simply her temperament, and her nose size was a genetic hand-me-down from her dad (who also endured verbal abuse as a child). And why did I have to have a rug head in high school when long shag-carpet haircuts were in? Does God have some sick sense of humor, or what? Does he look down on earth and say to the angels, "Watch this," and then zap some poor soul with a Pinocchio nose or a distracting birthmark? Does God give some girls a Barbie figure and saddle others with more of a Jabba the Hut frame just for kicks? What about you? What goes through your mind every morning when you greet your face in the mirror? Would you like to send your body back to the Manufacturer?

On the Lines

1. One of the most important principles of life is that you must always interpret the things you *don't* understand in light of the things you do understand. This is especially true when it comes to God and his Word. Write out the main thing that you do understand about God and his love from the previous chapter of this study. Think hard. Be honest.

_____

_____

_____

_____

2. Now, using what you've just written as the foundation for this chapter, let's continue. Is Jesus Christ someone you admire? I mean, if you could, would you really want to be like him?

☐ yes, I would   ☐ no, I would not

3. Let's take a peek at a passage in the Bible which many scholars believe gives us insight into what Jesus looked like. Turn to Isaiah 53. What do you think the statements about Jesus in verse 2 mean? Write out these statements in your own words:

_____

_____

_____

4. Would you *still* want to be like Jesus, if you could?

☐ yes, I would   ☐ no, I would not

5. Now, let's get a little more personal. Below are phrases from Psalm 139 from *The Living Bible*. Write out in your own words what each of these verses means about you. Take some time and think hard before you write your answer. Be specific about *yourself* whenever possible.

What God Says	*What It Means About Me*
"You made all the delicate, inner parts of my body, and knit them together in my mother's womb."	_____ _____ _____
"Thank you for making me so wonderfully complex! It is amazing to think about. Your workmanship is marvelous— and how well I know it."	_____ _____ _____

"You were there while I was
being formed in utter
seclusion."

_____

_____

_____

"You saw me before I was born
and scheduled each day of my
life before I began to breathe.
Every day was recorded in your
Book!"

_____

_____

_____

6. Look over your answers to questions 1 and 5. What conclusion must you and I come to, if both of these questions are dealing with the truth?

_____

_____

_____

Between the Lines

1. If we have low opinions of ourselves, and as Christians also believe that the way we are is God's doing, it can be easy to build up doubts about his love, or even bitterness toward him. Search your own heart right now. Do you harbor doubt about God's competency, or bitterness because you aren't who or what you'd like to be? Take some time right now and talk to the Lord. Tell him that you have mistakenly chosen to interpret his love in light of your own struggle, rather than the other way around. Ask for his forgiveness and help.

2. There are four main areas where we seem to struggle with who or what we are. They are:

* the way we look (our appearance)
* what we can do (our abilities)

* family (who our parents are)
* our surroundings (people, places, etc.)

Put a check beside the two that you feel are the hardest for you to accept as God's best for you:

☐ appearance   ☐ abilities

☐ family   ☐ surroundings

Now, go back to question 5 of "On the Lines." Look over your paraphrases of the verses from Psalm 139. How does what you wrote there deal with the two areas you checked above? Write out below four possible reasons why God deliberately made you the way he did or placed you where you are:

1. _____

2. _____

3. _____

4. _____

I would venture to guess that somewhere in your room is a tape collection, a pile of music cassettes that you punch into your stereo whenever you get the urge. Did you know that your *mind* has a "tape collection" too? It contains the messages we say to ourselves, about ourselves. Chances are you have some tapes of this latter sort that you need to stop playing to yourself. Like the tape that says, "I'm so ugly." Or the tapes that say, "I'm so stupid," "I'm so clumsy," "I'm such a wimp," "No one would ever want to be my friend,"—and the list goes on and on.

I want you to start spinning some *new* tapes! I want you to start telling yourself the truth about who and what God says you are. Look again at your answer to question 6 in "On the Lines." Figure out some way to transform this truth into a new tape you can play into your thoughts instead of the old ones. As you "record" and "play" these truths, you will find that the faulty messages will have less and less control over you.

Closing Lines

The comments of others can be a source of laughter for them but a cause of pain for us. My wife is now in her thirties and can recall vividly the coarse comments and jokes that made her their focus. She still sometimes struggles when people tell her she's too sensitive. I've gotten to the place where I refuse to use the word "too" when describing anything about anyone. Except for sin, people are what God created them to be.

For many months Jill carried a 3x5 card with her containing a positive statement about her sensitivity, rather that a cynical slam. Her thinking slowly changed. Jill's sensitivity is now her greatest strength. She has learned to use it to help others who are hurting. And now, you wonder about her nose? Jill just laughs when she journeys in her thoughts back to junior high. My brother is an ENT (ears, nose, throat) surgeon and could successfully repair and beautify this "faulty" feature. But Jill just isn't interested anymore. Her thinking has changed, and what once crippled her emotionally now has no control. We both joke about our "beaks" (mine is not exactly a button either), and the past pain is genuinely gone. Our features haven't changed—our *focus* has.

It's only when we make the values and views of people around us the measuring stick of our own worth that we forget that who and what we are is the result of thoughtful, loving planning on the part of the God of all creation. God wasn't out having lunch or on a scenic drive when your body and abilities came down the "assembly line"! There are no "manufacturer's defects" when it comes to who and what you are, or who and what I am. I am trying to be as gentle as possible when I say this, but . . . rejecting yourself for who and what you are is a subtle way of mocking God's work. That's an awesome thought, but chew on it for a while.

Lifeline:

Who I am is the result of the careful, loving plan of God himself.

His Lines

Psalm 139:14

1 Corinthians 15:10a

The Bottom Line (For Group Discussion)

1. Why do we always seem to lose whenever we listen to others in our search for self-worth?

2. Another enemy in our struggle for self-worth is Satan himself. He is called the "father of lies" (John 8:44) and the "accuser of the brethren" (Revelation 12:10). The Bible also says that he "deceives the whole world" (Revelation 12:9, TLB). Discuss each of these three negative ministries Satan can have in our lives in the area of thinking properly about who and what we are. How does he do it?

3. As a group, study Moses' call from God in Exodus 3. Moses certainly had difficulty accepting God's challenge because of how he saw himself. Did God seek to build up Moses' self-worth? What did he do instead? Why is this so significant?

4. Have members of the group write out on 3x5 cards the one thing that others say or do that most damages their view of themselves. Put the cards into a hat and let the group leader read them. Discuss how each person could help this individual see himself or herself as God sees them. (Note: warn each member not to share something so specific that everyone will immediately know who it is. Also, names should not be included.)

5. Secure a copy of the video production, "Hi-Tops" (the address is at the end of this chapter) and watch it as a group. Ask each group member to answer these two questions:

> 1. Toward whom did your own attitude change the most from the beginning of the film to the end? Why?

2.With whom did you feel that you could identify most in the film, and why? (Note: the characters in the film are all deliberate exaggerations, so a total identification will not occur.)

"Hi-Tops" is available from: Maranatha Music!
                                    P.O. Box 1396
                                    Costa Mesa, CA 92628

5

The Black Hole

Opening Lines

Black holes are a fascinating phenomenon. Scientists are still bewildered as to their origin and function. What exists is a section of space with a gravitational pull so strong that even light cannot escape. That's what I call suction! In fact, the term itself is becoming a synonym for things that seem to draw everything else into themselves.

Bobbie had become a "black hole" personality type. A transfer student her senior year, she had to go through all the rituals that make one a part of the student body, such as winning new friends and walking that delicate line between confidence and cockiness. Unfortunately, Bobbie didn't make the grade with the other senior students. Because I had her for only one hour each day, it took almost a semester before I'd had enough exposure to her to determine the source of her difficulty.

Bobbie was arrogant, rude, and insensitive. As far as she was concerned, the universe began and ended with her needs. At least that was the impression she gave. She was like a living, breathing black hole. It was almost impossible to be in her presence without being sucked in. As I got to know her better, however, I discovered that beneath the offensive veneer was a caring, stimulating, deep individual. She was nothing like the image she created in the minds of her peers. In talking with her, I learned some sobering statistics about her childhood. She had no natural parents. She had been raised by relatives before finally being adopted at age eight.

She had a daughter from a relationship she had had prior to coming to our school; so she had to balance being both a mother and a high school senior. As far as Bobbie was concerned, God had dealt her a pretty crummy hand in the game called life.

But I knew of other students who had suffered just as painful a childhood as Bobbie's, who weren't on the weekly "Who's Who" list at school, yet were able to lead positive and others-centered lives. Why was Bobbie so bitter and rude? What is it that causes one person to weather pain and yet develop a winsome personality while another person degenerates into an offensive pest? Would it have helped Bobbie if she had a better sense of self-worth? Was she spiteful to others because she didn't love herself enough?

On the Lines

We've spent four chapters examining the critical value of possessing a proper sense of self-worth. Now we need to examine what I call the "dark side" of self-worth. It is true that our person needs result from being made in the image of a personal God, and are therefore designed to be met; it is also true (as with anything) that an over-emphasis on self-worth can become destructive and evil.

1. Isaiah 14:12-15 is commonly accepted as God's description of what caused Satan's fall from heaven. Satan was created by God as a beautiful angel, but something very interesting occurred. Look up this passage and read it two or three times, then answer the questions below:

   (1) How many times does the word "I" appear in this short passage? _____ What do you think is the significance of that?

   _____

   _____

   _____

(2) What things did Satan want that led to his eventual downfall? List as many as you can, and try to put them in today's terms:

_____

_____

_____

_____

_____

2. Paul makes some startling statements in 2 Timothy 3:1-5. Look up those verses and use the information you find to answer the questions below. (Note: In the Bible, the term "last days" can refer to the time period beginning with Jesus' birth and ending with his second coming; but it can also refer to the period just before the end of the world, when things will get worse and worse.)

a. How does Paul describe these last days?

_____

b. What do you think Paul means by that?

_____

_____

c. What does Paul say will cause these last days to be such terrible times?

_____

_____

d. What do you think that means?

_____

_____

3. What does Jesus say will result when a person makes himself the focus of all his attentions and desires? (Mark 8:34-36)

_____

_____

If the person doesn't actually die physically, what else might Jesus mean when he says that this person will lose his life?

_____

_____

_____

Between the Lines

1. One of the surest ways to determine whether or not you are becoming a "black hole" personality is to measure the amount of time you spend talking about yourself. It's not wrong to talk about ourselves, but, on the other hand, we tend to talk most about what we think is most important. Here's what we want you to do for one school week:

DAY #1	Don't talk about yourself for one hour or one lunch period.	
DAY #2	Don't talk about yourself for two hours.	
DAY #3	Don't talk about yourself for half a day.	
DAY #4	Don't talk about yourself for half a day.	
DAY #5	Don't talk about yourself for an entire day!	

Ground Rules: "Talking about yourself" includes initiating conversation about yourself, your appearance, grades, problems and so forth. It's okay to answer questions directed to you about yourself.

Also, recruit a friend who will give you a mutually agreed upon signal if and when you do start talking about yourself.

2.The second project, to be done at the same time as the first, is to ask the people you are talking with about themselves and their lives. (Suggestions: Ask about their feelings, activities, family, athletics, and so on.) Follow the schedule below:

DAY #1	Ask three questions.	Check here when done. ☐
DAY #2	Ask three questions.	Check here when done. ☐
DAY #3	Ask six questions.	Check here when done. ☐
DAY #4	Ask six questions.	Check here when done. ☐
DAY #5	Ask ten questions.	Check here when done. ☐

3. If you discover that you are spending too much time talking and thinking about yourself, tell the Lord. Tell him that you are finding yourself doing the same thing Satan did, focusing on the "I." Ask his forgiveness, and give him the liberty to remind you whenever you become too self-centered.

Closing Lines

The sorrow and pain that resulted in Bobbie's rudeness was not the consequence of growing up in a less-than-perfect home. Neither was it the fruit of her own past sins. Her condition was the result of her preoccupation with herself and her wants and her needs. Bobbie talked only about herself. If she spoke of others, it was usually about what they had done to her. It has been said that the smallest package in the world is a person wrapped up in herself. That was Bobbie!

I tried on numerous occasions to steer her gaze toward the needs of others. But I never succeeded. She graduated and is gone, a miserable bundle of self. It's strange. Our need for self-worth is real and must be met. That's the way God planned it. But, it must be met by God. Whenever we seek to saturate the self within, it becomes a black hole that sucks our entire being into its vortex. The gravitational pull on those around us is great, and we cannot see out or get out. Self-worth is a legitimate need, but so is food. Taken to an extreme, both can become self-destructive. We are living in an age when everyone is preoccupied with the idea of self. The media promote the idolatry of self. In fact, there is even a magazine by that name! Jesus' statement about losing our life if we spend our time trying to save it is true. Self is a black hole. Don't get too near the edge!

Lifeline:

A preoccupation with self will destroy me.

His Lines

Mark 8:34-36

1 John 2:16

The Bottom Line (For Group Discussion)

1. Discuss how the assignments in the "Between the Lines" section went for each member of the group. What was the hardest? Easiest? What lessons were learned? How did others respond?

2. Have members of the group bring their favorite song (with the lyrics) to the group meeting. Discuss the focus of the song. Is its focus on *self?*

3. Assign each group member the task of bringing the best magazine advertisement they can find that promotes self-preoccupation. Have them explain:

    (1) Why they chose that particular ad;

    (2) What they see as the message of the ad;

    (3) Whether they think it is good or bad, and why.

4. Is it possible for things like aerobics and physical fitness to get out of hand? Explain. If so, what might be some guidelines?

6

Givers Finders, Keepers Losers

Opening Lines

One of the possible pitfalls of a Christian high school is what I call the "pipeline perspective." If you're born into a Christian home, go to a Christian church, have Christian friends, attend a Christian school, go to a Christian college, work for a Christian firm, marry a Christian, join a Christian church, put your kids in a Christian school, and are buried in a Christian cemetery, it's easy for your Christian faith to be pretty faithless. It's like crawling in one end of an enormous pipeline and finally coming out the other side without seeing or experiencing anything besides "pipe." I've discovered that the students at our school will become bored with God (sounds absurd, doesn't it?) if left only to themselves and their world. But I have also found that high school students can choose to channel their energies beyond the sacred halls. If they exercise their faith rather than just read about it, they grow. They have a purpose that isn't based on gaining popularity. Their faith is fueled and fostered, and they are happier. It's an on-going process. They can *feel* it. They "catch the wave."

Several years ago I helped start a club that we called "The Voice of Amos." Amos was an Old Testament prophet who spoke to the people of Israel against social injustice. Our organization was designed to be a "voice" against the social injustices of our day, such as abortion, mercy-killing, and any legislation that cheapened or attacked the dignity of mankind as the image-bearer of God. We became involved in things like letter-writing campaigns and passive boycotts. We were watching Washington and wanted our voice to be heard when we disagreed. We wrote senators and congressmen about our feelings on issues that would influence the future of any present high school student. One such item involved a major pharmaceutical company which was researching a chemical that would allow women to abort their babies at home! These activities were exciting and fun. But something quite unexpected happened. The students who were actively involved became more committed to their Christian faith. They had a renewed vitality in their eyes that replaced the glossed-over look that had sometimes been there before.

Why did this happen? What was it that transformed a handful of complacent high school sophomores into caring, committed Christians who were living out their faith, taking risks? I would have to say that a large percentage probably struggled with personal self-worth. They weren't born leaders or confident "quarterbacks" who carried the ball in any area of school life. They weren't in the "in crowd." What was it that prompted these students to resist preoccupation with themselves and, consequently, avoid the "black hole" we examined in the last chapter? Is there really a concrete and practical way to escape becoming engulfed in the web of self-centeredness? If so, what is it?

On the Lines

1. Let's look back at a verse you studied in the last chapter, Mark 8:35. We examined what Jesus said will happen to those who center their lives around themselves. Look at this verse again. What does Jesus say is the way to "find" ourselves?

_____

_____

What do you think this involves, practically speaking, for you and me?

_____

_____

_____

2. Probably the two best examples of this perspective on life, other than Jesus, are John the Baptist and the Apostle Paul. Look up each of the following passages and write out what you think the goal in life was for each of these two men:

John the Baptist (John 3:30)

_____

_____

The Apostle Paul (2 Corinthians 4:5)

_____

_____

Why do you think Paul would say something like this?

_____

4. Jesus told his disciples a truth that is tucked away in the Book of Acts. The word "blessed" means "happy" or "to be envied." Look up Acts 20:35. What is the principle that Jesus gives us here?

_____

How do you think this applies to us in regard to focusing all our attention on ourselves?

_____

Can we be happy (blessed) if we spend our time trying to be happy? Why or why not?

_____

_____

5. Many high school students (maybe you!) are in a state of depression over who and what they are. An exciting truth for you is found in Isaiah 58:10,11. What does this verse say is a cure for the depression that comes from focusing on ourselves?

_____

_____

_____

Who could the "hungry" and "oppressed" people be in your life? (I seriously doubt that you will need to think beyond the doors of your school or church.) Be specific!

_____

_____

6. Summarize below what new perspectives you have gained from this chapter about your quest for self-worth. Be as personal and thorough as you can.

_____

_____

_____

_____

Between the Lines

1. Look back at the second part of your answer to question 5 above. Who were the people you listed as the "hungry" or "oppressed" in your life? What can you do *this* week to be faithful to the instructions of Isaiah 58:10,11? I want you to write out specifically what, when, and how you will do this:

What I intend to do:

_____

_____

For whom I will do it:

_____

_____

When I intend to do it:

_____

_____

This doesn't mean a lifetime commitment to a lonely peer or classmate. Often a phone call, sharing a pizza, or just communicating that you really care and want to listen when you ask, "How are you?" is all it takes. For example, Jill and I were reading in bed late one night after a discouraging week. The phone rang. The familiar long distance hum gave way to a former student's voice far away at college. "Mr. Sciacca?" she said, "How are you and Jill? I've really been burdened to pray for you." Our light was rekindled and hers glowed.

Closing Lines

What was it that lessened the tendency among my "Voice of Amos" students to succumb to the black hole of self-preoccupation? I believe that they discovered the truth of what Jesus meant when he said, "It is more blessed to give than to receive." The joy they experienced by serving others outweighed the tempting tug to focus inward. As long as they were involved in "The Voice of Amos," their normal battle for self-worth was minimized. It appears to me that one of the best defenses against the black hole of self is servanthood. One could even go so far as to say that genuine servanthood stems from and produces a healthy sense of self-worth.

Let me bring up one final point: God's ultimate goal in your life is not a solid sense of self-worth. His deepest desire and goal is that you *know* him, and that you reflect his character to the world—and to all the big and little people around you. His desires for your life, if you make them your desires too, will ultimately bring you the happiness and fulfillment you are seeking. God told Jeremiah something that speaks loudly about our battle in the arena of self-worth:

> Let not the wise man bask in his wisdom, nor the mighty man in his might, nor the rich man in his riches. Let them boast in *this* alone: that they truly know *me,* and understand that I am the Lord of justice and of righteousness whose love is steadfast; and that I love to be this way. (Jeremiah 9:23,24, TLB, emphasis mine)

If you really want to discover who you are and be able to rejoice in that discovery, then give yourself away! Remember, it is that person who "loses" himself who "finds" himself, while the one who spends his life looking for himself will end his search still looking, never finding.

There's one more thing you need to know. The pain and pressure of searching for self-worth in high school will not follow you into college or the work world. It's true that self-worth is a life-long struggle. But the intensity and hurt that go with it in high school pretty much evaporate when you graduate. On the other hand, learning how to reach out beyond yourself and touch the needs of those around you is a skill that will profit you forever. The earlier you embrace this truth, the sooner your sun will shine in the darkness. It will make you a sensitive husband or wife, a caring parent, a valued employee, and most of all, you will one day win the most esteemed prize of all—the statement, "Well done, good and faithful servant" (Matthew 25:21, NIV) from the lips of Jesus himself.

Lifeline:

Self-sacrifice is the path to self-discovery.

His Lines

Jeremiah 9:23,24)

Isaiah 58:10,11)

The Bottom Line (For Group Discussion)

1. Is there a place in your community for something like "The Voice of Amos?" If you are interested in becoming active as a group for the rights of the poor, oppressed and helpless in your city, contact the following ministries for possible ideas:

PRISON FELLOWSHIP (writing to prisoners)
P.O. Box 17500
Washington, D.C. 20041-0500

CHRISTIAN ACTION COUNCIL (pro-life activities)
701 West Broad Street
Suite 405
Falls Church, VA 22046-9990

FOCUS ON THE FAMILY (pro-family activities)
801 Corporate Center Drive
Pomona, CA 91768

2. The contemporary Christian rock group Petra has begun a correspondence program called Prayer Warriors, to "encourage youth to take up their mightiest weapon in the spiritual battle—

prayer." Interested groups will be paired with another group across the country and then use ideas suggested by Petra to join their prayer lives together. Write to:

> Petra
> P.O. Box 190
> Nashville, TN, 37202.

3. Another Christian rock group, DeGarmo and Key, has compiled four music videos that emphasize missions. The package contains four music videos, Bible studies, activity guides and footage of the group's recent trip to Africa. Write to:

> Video Coordinator, Benson Company
> 365 Great Circle Road
> Nashville, TN 37228.

4. Perhaps your group could develop a baby-sitting ministry. You could give it a catchy name, and volunteer to baby-sit for young couples in your church or community.

5. Exactly *why* is it "more blessed to give than to receive"?

6. Have group members share, if they are willing, what each of them learned from the exercise in "Between the Lines."

7. Who are the "hungry" or "oppressed" (i.e., orphans, widows, divorcées) in your church? What could your group do, on a practical level, to help?

8. Have someone in your group meet with the pastor and find out what your church is doing for widows. Discuss in your group what more could be done, and how you might fit in the solution. A study of 1 Timothy 5 might be rewarding and enlightening.